In memory of my friend
Wendy Challenger
H.B.

za tebe
M.S.

First published in Great Britain in 2019
by Boxer Books Limited.
www.boxerbooks.com

The illustrations were prepared using acrylic paints and soft pencil.
The text is set in Providence Sans Pro.

ISBN: 978-1-912757-09-1

1 3 5 7 9 10 8 6 4 2

Printed in Malaysia

All of our papers are sourced from managed forests and renewable resources.

POLAR BEAR'S STORY

WRITTEN BY HARRIET BLACKFORD

ILLUSTRATED BY MANJA STOJIC

BOXER BOOKS

Polar Bear is
small, white
and fluffy.
Her fur is so
thick and her
skin is so fat
that she can
live in the
cold, cold Arctic.

Polar Bear and her brother tumble out of their mother's snow den for the first time. They see the cold Arctic sky above and the crunchy white snow under their feet. Time to play!

Polar Bear's mother is hungry. She hasn't eaten all winter so she leads her cubs off across the snowy land in search of food. When Polar Bear is hungry she feeds on her mother's rich milk.

Polar Bear sees the Arctic fox peep over a snowy hill and hears the noisy seabirds overhead.

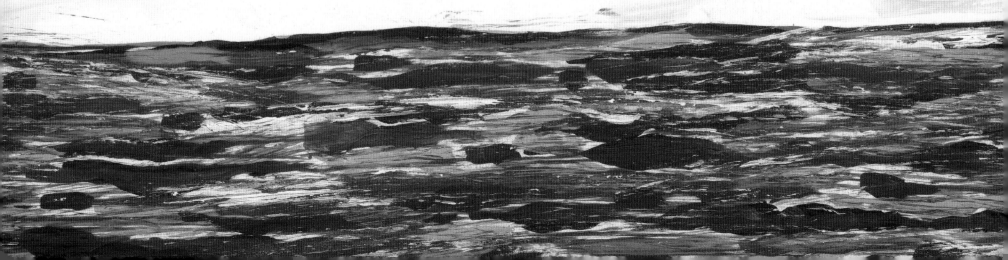

Seals are watching the polar bears as the polar bears sniff the air and watch them.

Polar Bear has the best
nose ever and can smell
a seal in the sea
under the thick ice.

There are holes in the ice where the seals
come up to breathe when the sea is frozen.

Polar Bear's mother
waits and watches.
Polar Bear and her
brother watch
and learn.

Polar Bear is getting bigger and
catching food for herself more often.

She is on her own for days hunting on the frozen sea. She sees a group of walruses lazing on the ice. They would make a tasty dinner, but they are so big!

Polar Bear creeps up
to a small one. She is
so busy watching
it she does
not notice
its mother.

Suddenly, the huge, angry mother rears up and lunges at Polar Bear with her sharp tusks.

Polar Bear scoots out of the way just in time.

It's not easy catching your own dinner!

Polar Bear does not mind the freezing cold.

When the wind blows too strongly she curls up to keep warm. But when the days grow warmer she gets too hot, so she rests in a shady den. Worse still, the sea ice melts and she cannot find any seal breathing holes. Polar Bear starts to feel very hungry.

Polar Bear has roamed a long way trying
to find something to eat and is so hungry
she tries to catch the noisy seabirds.

One day her nose
tells her there is
something edible
nearby.

She finds the leftovers of a dead seal
and rushes up to start chewing.
It's not much but it is food.

Suddenly, she hears a loud growling.

The biggest polar bear she has ever seen
is coming straight for her. Polar Bear
might be 'dinner' if she does not move fast
enough! But she is so very hungry.
She grabs one more mouthful and runs.

It's getting colder. Polar Bear sees the Arctic fox and the noisy seabirds.

She can see seals swimming around the ice floes. The sea is getting icy again. It will not be long before Polar Bear can walk out onto the frozen sea and hunt once more.

POLAR BEAR'S STORY
A note from the author

This is the story of a polar bear cub growing up and learning how to take care of herself.

Polar bears are the biggest bears in the world. A big male can weigh as much as eight grown men and can be two and a half metres long. Measure this against your sofa or your bed to get an idea of his size.

Polar bears live on the ice-covered seas surrounding the North Pole called the Arctic. They are very well suited to their icy world as they have small ears that don't stick out into the cold air, very thick fat under their skin and big feet to help them to swim and to walk on thin ice. Polar bears are very good swimmers.

Polar bears have a hard time finding enough food in the summer as the sea ice melts and they cannot hunt seals. They can go a long time without eating. However, hunting is getting more difficult as the sea ice is melting much faster than it used to and is taking longer to ice up again. Most scientists say this is due to global warming, which means our planet's climate is changing very quickly. Burning coal and pollution are the main causes. Scientists think polar bears may be in trouble because the place where they live is changing so fast. We can all help by choosing ways to live that are less harmful to our planet.